# What Do We Know About Habitats?

1. Think about your home. What makes it a good and safe place to live?

   _____
   _____

2. Think of a wild animal that you know some facts about. Draw and write about a suitable habitat for the animal you have chosen.

# Different Habitats

1. Find out about animals that live in a woodland, a river and the sea. Draw and label two that live in each habitat.

**woodland**

**river**

**sea**

# Habitats

**2** Choose one of the animals that lives in the woodland. Why is this a suitable habitat for it?

_____
_____
_____
_____

**3** Choose one of the animals that lives in the river. Why is this a suitable habitat for it?

_____
_____
_____
_____

**4** Choose one of the animals that lives in the sea. Why is this a suitable habitat for it?

_____
_____
_____
_____

# Habitats

5  Find out about plants that live in a woodland, a river and the sea. Draw and label two that live in each of the habitats.

| woodland |
|---|
|  |

| river |
|---|
|  |

| sea |
|---|
|  |

6  What is similar about all the plants?

_____

# Rainforests and Oceans

1. Choose a plant and animal that live in the rainforest. List three facts about each of them.

| Plant _____ | Animal _____ |
|---|---|
|  |  |
|  |  |
|  |  |

2. Choose a plant and animal that live in the ocean. List three facts about each of them.

| Plant _____ | Animal _____ |
|---|---|
|  |  |
|  |  |
|  |  |

# Extreme Habitats

1 Draw and label a plant and an animal that live in the polar regions.

2 Draw and label a plant and an animal that live in the desert.

# Micro-habitats

1a  Draw a picture to show how birds make their home in a tree.

1b  Why is a tree suitable habitat for a bird?

2  Under a log is a micro-habitat. List some living things you might find there.

# Contrasting Habitats

1. Find out about homes built by different animals. Choose two. Draw their homes and write about how the animals build them.

# Habitats

**2** What is the difference between the habitat for the pet snake and the habitat for the goldfish?

**3a** If you could have a new pet what would you choose?

**3b** Make a shopping list of the things you need to buy to give it a suitable home.

# Minibeast Safari

1. What minibeasts can you find where you live? Draw and label four common ones.

# Science Skills

**Graph it!**
This tally chart shows what Class 2 found on their 'minibeast safari'.

| Type of minibeast | Tally | Number found |
|---|---|---|
| Earthworm | ||| | |
| Spider | || | |
| Woodlouse | ||||| | | |
| Ant | ||||| |||| | |
| Snail | |||| | |
| Ladybird | | | |

1  Complete the table to show how many of each type they found.

2  Draw a block graph showing these results. Label the graph. The first one has been done for you.

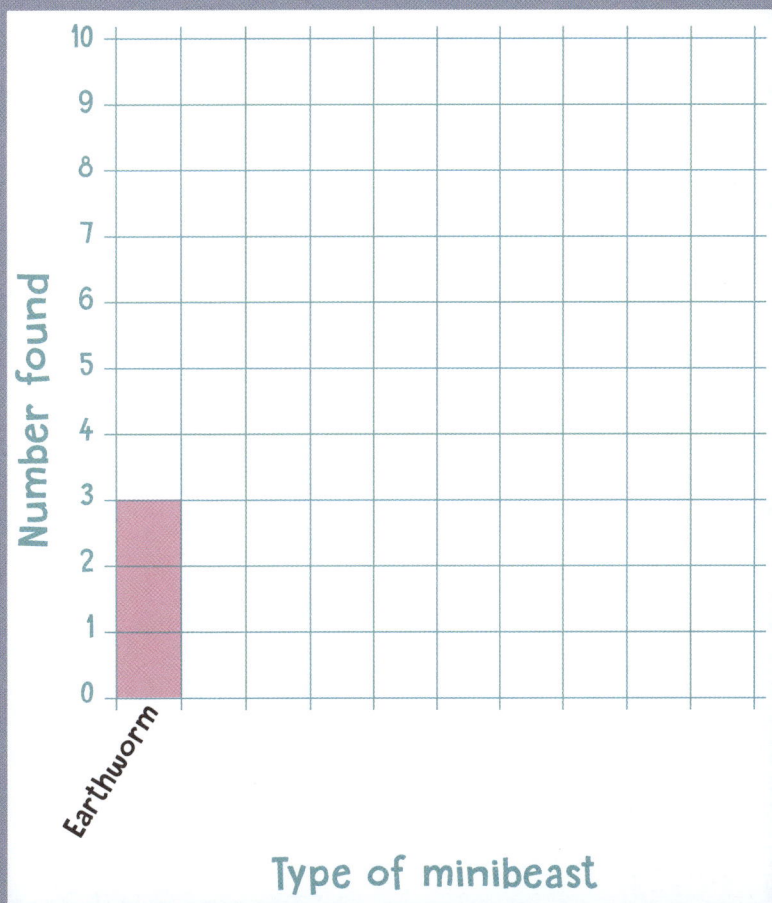

# Habitats

3  Go on your own minibeast safari. Complete a tally chart to show what you found.

| Type of minibeast | Tally | Number found |
|---|---|---|
| | | |
| | | |
| | | |
| | | |
| | | |
| | | |

4  Draw and label a block graph showing the results.

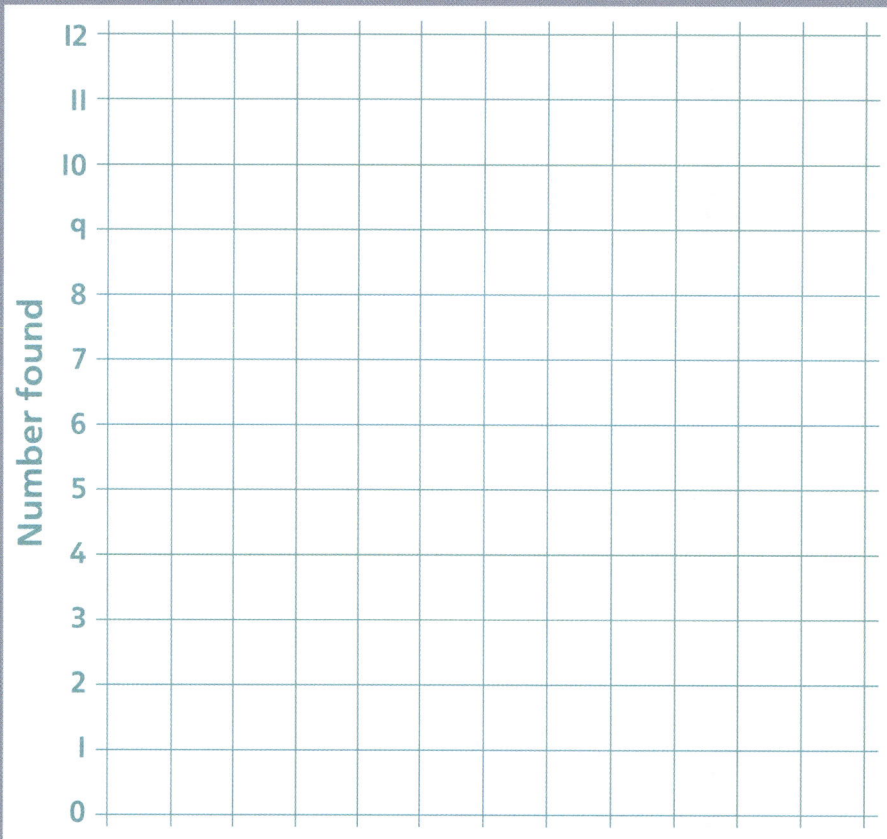

# Minibeasts in a Pond

1 Find out about some minibeasts that have a pond as their habitat.

2a Draw a pond.

2b Draw the minibeasts in the part of the pond that is their habitat.

2c Label the minibeasts.

# Suitable Habitats

1. Look at the list of animals in the table. Record the type of habitat that they live in, and name something they eat.

2. List a plant that also lives in the same habitat.

| Animal | Type of habitat | Eats | Plant |
|---|---|---|---|
| Camel | Desert | Most plants | Cacti |
| Dolphin | | | |
| Penguin | | | |
| Trout | | | |
| Whirligig beetle | | | |
| Sloth | | | |
| Crow | | | |
| Woodlouse | | | |

3. Draw an earthworm with several segments and write a different fact about it on each segment.

# Building Habitats

1  List four endangered animals.

   1 _____
   2 _____
   3 _____
   4 _____

2  Find out more about one of these animals. Write about it. Include why it became endangered.

# Perfect Habitat

1. Think about what you have learned about habitats. Choose a plant or animal and think about the things it needs in its habitat. Plan a poster to advertise a perfect habitat for your plant or animal. Include a picture of the habitat and its key features.

# Fuel curiosity, spark imagination.

**UK National Curriculum YEAR 2** | **CAMBRIDGE primary Stages 1, 2, 3** | **Pearson iPRIMARY YEAR 2, 3, 5**

*Science Bug International* is an exciting and comprehensive science programme that has been designed to make sure your children never stop asking questions about their world!

This Workbook contains questions from the Topic Book plus additional questions to reinforce and extend learning.

With full and comprehensive coverage of the skills and knowledge required for curriculum attainment, *Science Bug International* will help you to nurture and inspire your young scientist.

Series editor: Deborah Herridge
Author: Debbie Eccles

www.pearsonschools.co.uk
myorders@pearson.com

ISBN 978-0-435-19600-4

# Workbook
# Living Things

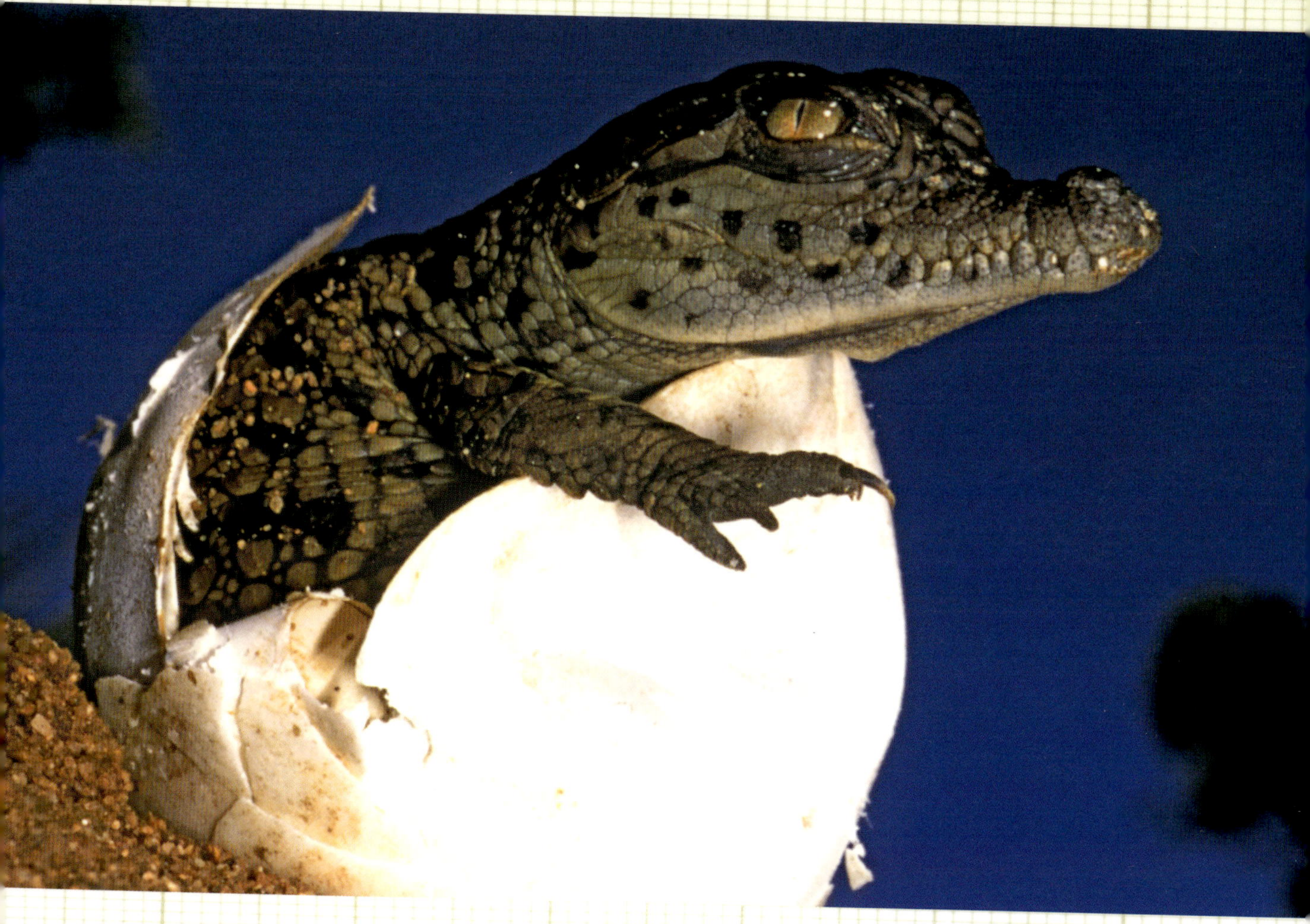

Published by Pearson Education Limited, 80 Strand, London, WC2R 0RL.

www.pearsonschools.co.uk

Text © Pearson Education Limited 2018
Edited by Just Content Ltd
Typeset by PDQ Media
Original illustrations © Pearson Education Limited 2018
Illustrated by PDQ Media
Picture research by Integra
Cover photo/illustration © **Alamy: WILDLIFE GmbH**

First published 2018

22
11

**British Library Cataloguing in Publication Data**
A catalogue record for this book is available from the British Library

ISBN 9780435196646

**Copyright notice**
All rights reserved. No part of this publication may be reproduced in any form or by any means (including photocopying or storing it in any medium by electronic means and whether or not transiently or incidentally to some other use of this publication) without the written permission of the copyright owner, except in accordance with the provisions of the Copyright, Designs and Patents Act 1988 or under the terms of a licence issued by the Copyright Licensing Agency, Barnards Inn, 86 Fetter Lane, London EC4A IEN(www.cla.co.uk). Applications for the copyright owner's written permission should be addressed to the publisher.

Printed in the UK by Bell & Bain Ltd, Glasgow

**Note from the publisher**
Pearson has robust editorial processes, including answer and fact checks, to ensure the accuracy of the content in this publication, and every effort is made to ensure this publication is free of errors. We are, however, only human, and occasionally errors do occur. Pearson is not liable for any misunderstandings that arise as a result of errors in this publication, but it is our priority to ensure that the content is accurate. If you spot an error, please do contact us at resourcescorrections@pearson.com so we can make sure it is corrected.